DREAMWORKS

pi kids® phoenix international publications, inc.

Shrek misses his days of being a feared ogre! Now he is a family man, liked by everyone in town. When Rumpelstiltskin offers Shrek a deal to trade a day from his past to be a "real ogre" for a day, Shrek gladly accepts. Before Shrek signs on the dotted line, can you find some of Rumpel's favorite things?

curly-toed shoes

this quill pen

jar of magic ink

miniature disco ball

this pile of contracts

plate of roasted rat

slug and tonic mix

spinning wheel

Shrek finds a way to break Rumpel's wicked spell. He magically appears back in his real life with Fiona...smack-dab in the middle of the triplet's terrific birthday bash! Can you find these friends and family members at the party?

Fergus

Farkle

Queen Lillian

Gingy

Felicia

Three Blind Mice

Big Bad Wolf

Pinocchio

Washed ashore on Madagascar, Alex, Marty, Melman, and Gloria think they're in San Diego. But when they meet King Julien, they realize how far away from home they really are! Look around and find the zoo buddies and their new friends:

Maurice

Gloria

Melman

King Julien

Alex

Marty

Alex, Marty, Melman, and Gloria want to get back to New York City, but in the meantime they'll put on the best circus show they can! See if you can spot their new circus friends:

Stefano

this elephant

Vitaly

Sonia

this horse

this dog

The Viking village of Berk is under attack — by dragons! The brave Vikings are doing all they can to protect their homes, but the dragons are very powerful. If only young Hiccup could help! As the villagers wage war, keep a lookout for these different types of dragons:

this Gronkle

Night Fury

this Deadly Nadder

this Monstrous Nightmare

Terrible Terror

this Hideous Zippleback

Over the last five years, Hiccup has taught his Viking village the true nature of dragons. Now they live peacefully side by side, and enjoy a new activity together—Dragon Racing! While Hiccup and Toothless are out exploring, find these brave young racers and their fans:

Fishlegs

Astrid

Ruffnut

Tuffnut

Stoick the Vast

Gobber

P o, Tigress, Monkey, Viper, Mantis, and Crane can't practice all the time. Sometimes they just need to be silly. Today Master Shifu breaks up the fun with a warning—Tai Lung has escaped from prison! Before Po and the Furious Five leave, find these things around the dining hall:

lantern

these chopsticks

teacup

stack of bowls

artwork

vase

Now it's time for Po to get serious! With his training and understanding of the nature of limitless power, Po is set to defeat Tai Lung and become the Dragon Warrior. While the foes battle, look around for these shop items:

this bucket

this spoon

scroll

this candle

this wok

this teapot

Rumpelstiltskin is secretly plotting against Shrek. Go back to Rumpel's carriage and find these warning signs that Shrek shouldn't trust Rumpel:

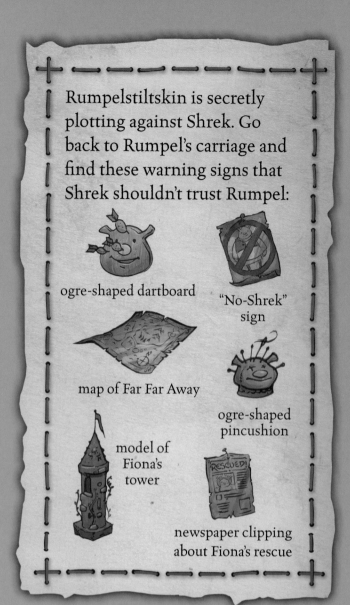

ogre-shaped dartboard

"No-Shrek" sign

map of Far Far Away

ogre-shaped pincushion

model of Fiona's tower

newspaper clipping about Fiona's rescue

Ogres have different tastes when it comes to party food. Head back for more birthday fun and find these not-so-tasty ogre treats:

eyeball salad

moldy cheese

mud cake

grub dip with bark chips

box of slug treats

squirmin' worms casserole

Hustle back to King Julien's party and find these party-lovin' lemurs:

Bounce back to the big top and find these circus props:

these rocket shoes

top hat

this ball

this helmet

this balloon

hoop

Hurry back to the burning town of Berk and find these valiant villagers:

Fly back to the arena and find these Dragon Racing things:

this helmet   black sheep   this pennant

this goal   this flag   white sheep

Follow your nose back to the dining hall and find these tantalizing foods:

potatoes

garlic   chili peppers   dumpling

eggs   bowl of noodles

Flip back to Po and Tai Lung's fight and find these firecrackers: